Silvey-Jex

RAVETTE PUBLISHING

First published by Ravette Publishing 2010.

Ravette Publishing Limited
PO Box 876
Horsham
West Sussex RH12 9GH

ISBN: 978-1-84161-332-1

IT'S OBVIOUSLY ONE OF THOSE BOOKS YOU CAN'T PUT DOWN
LAWN CARE
LAWN CARE

I CALL THAT "OVERKILL". ALL I SAID WAS - I THOUGHT I SAW A GREENFLY
SILVEY-JEX

THE TOMATOES ARE ALL BEHIND THIS YEAR BUT THEY'LL COME GOOD LATER ON. IT'S WHAT I CALL "TOMATO CATCH-UP"

DON'T GO UP THERE JACK

DOWN! DAMN YOU DOWN!
SILVEY-JEX

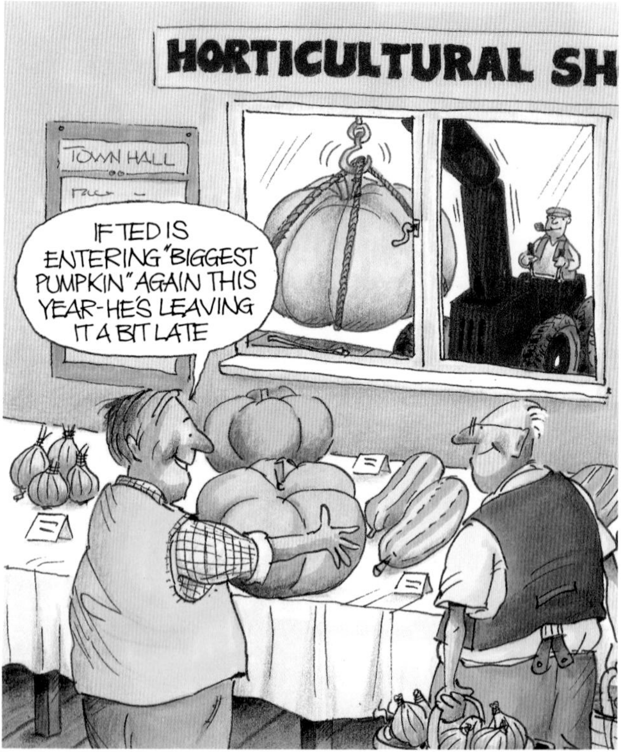
HORTICULTURAL SH
TOWN HALL
IF TED IS ENTERING "BIGGEST PUMPKIN" AGAIN THIS YEAR - HE'S LEAVING IT A BIT LATE

OKAY-NOW FOR A GENTLE FLOW, TURN THE KNOB TO THE RIGHT - SORRY - LEFT.
LION HEAD FOUNTAIN

BE AFRAID
BE VERY AFRAID
BUG KILLER
SILVEY-JEX

...AND THEY'VE ALL GOT COUNTRY NAMES MY DEARS... HERE'S DEVILS' SCROTUM, GRANNYS' KNICKERS, WHORES BOTTOM AND OLD MANS PHLEGM

CALL THAT
A FRUIT CAGE?
IT'S MORE LIKE
AN AVIARY

IT'S A BIT LATE TO ASK ME IF IT'S A WEED NOW YOU'VE PULLED IT UP

OH GOOD! YOU'VE FOUND THE TROWEL I LOST
SKUEY-JEX

JOYCE! REMEMBER THAT MUSHROOM SPAWN? ONLY ONE HAS COME UP
SILVEY-JEX

IT APPEARS THEY LIKED THE GARDEN SO MUCH THEY TOOK IT WITH THEM
SOLD

ONE THING I CAN'T STAND IS A DIRTY MOWER
WASH & WAX
SILVERTSER

ARE YOU GOING TO FOOL AROUND WITH THAT BIND-WEED ALL MORNING...OR DO YOU WANT SOME LUNCH?
SILVEY-JEX

GORDON'S VERY SQUEAMISH...HE'S JUST CUT A WORM IN HALF
SILVEY-JEX

YOU DAMAGE THAT TREE MY BOY AND YOU'RE IN BIG TROUBLE

ALRIGHT! ALRIGHT! YOU WIN...GET A NEW MOWER IF YOU MUST
TOOLS
SILVEY-JEX

THE GOOD THING ABOUT THIS LITTLE CHAP IS... HE'S GOT A VERY STRONG ROOT SYSTEM
SILVEY-JEX

SO THAT'S THE... "ENOUGH TO SEE THE FAMILY THROUGH THE WINTER" CROP IS IT?
SILVEY-JEX

GRANNY... LOOK WHAT GRANDAD'S DOING
JER

WELL, AT LEAST HE HASN'T COME UP IN THE LAWN
SILVEY-J

DO YOU HAVE TO USE THAT STINKING HORSE MANURE?
WHAT ELSE WOULD YOU PUT ON A HORSE CHESTNUT?
SILVEY-JEX

BE A GOOD LAD AND ASK YOUR MUM IF SHE COULD GIVE ME A HAND WITH THE TURF.... AND BE QUICK!

ER...AS YOU HAVEN'T USED THE MOWER I LENT YOU LAST YEAR-CAN I HAVE IT BACK?

GEORGE...
COME HERE
QUICK!!
SILVEY-JEX.

ARTHUR-
THE DOG'S DIGGING
IN THE GARDEN
AGAIN
SILVEY-JEX

SHRUBS
CLIMBERS
ROSES
SILVEY-JEX

IT'S SUCH A NICE DAY... WHY STAY INDOORS IRONING?
SILVEY-JEX

RIGHT! BEFORE I START CUTTING... WHERE DID YOU DO IT? SHOW ME...COME ON... WHERE IS IT?

...CHARMING LITTLE GARDEN... BIT OF A JUNGLE AT THE MOMENT OF COURSE...
FOR SALE

...SO I THOUGHT SEEING AS HE SPENT MOST OF HIS LIFE ON THE ALLOTMENT...
RROTS
ONIONS
BERT HOPKINS
LETTUCE
LEEKS

RODNEY- DO LOOK OUT FOR THAT BABY HEDGEHOG
SILVEY-JEX

IF YOU THINK I'M HAVING AFTERNOON TEA UNDER THAT, YOU'VE ANOTHER THINK COMING
SILVEY-JEX

SERVES YOU RIGHT FOR TURFING OVER THE POND

ANY NORMAL HUSBAND HAS A SHED. MINE'S GOT A WENDY HOUSE!
SILVEY-JEX

PLEASE
HELP
YOURSELF
PLEASE
PLEASE
HELP
YOURSELF
SILVEY-JEX.